Five Nice Beans

by Liza Charlesworth

ISBN: 978-1-338-84450-4

Art Director: Tannaz Fassihi; Designer: Cynthia Ng; Illustrated by Michael Robertson

3 4 5 6 68 26 25 24

Printed in Jiaxing, China. First printing, June 2022.

Meet five nice beans:
Mom, Dad, Rose, Tate,
and cute Duke.
Beans are a lot like people!

Beans wake up.
Wake,
wake,
wake.

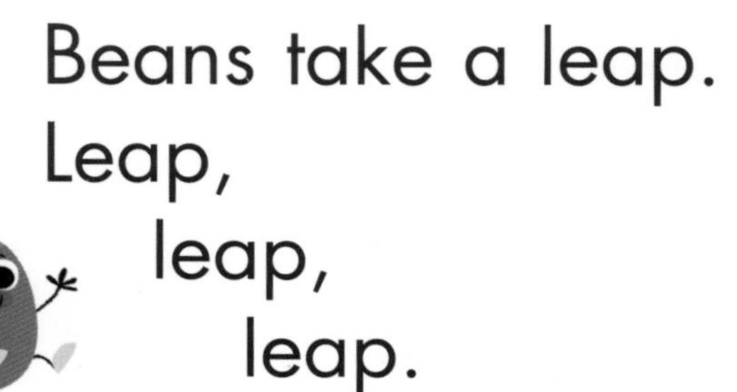

Beans take a leap.
Leap,
leap,
leap.

Beans ride a bike.
Bike, bike, bike.

Beans read a tale.
Read,
read,
read.

Beans eat a fine meal.
Eat, eat, eat.
"I see the sun!" says Dad.
"It is time to get on the road."

The five beans leap in a big jeep.
BEEP, BEEP!
They ride to a lake.

The lake is neat!
Rose can see a tail.
Tate can see a boat.
Duke can dig a deep hole.

Mom can see a HUGE ride.
The five beans feel brave
and take a seat on it.
Up, up, up, up, up...

At the tip top,
the five beans do NOT
feel a bit brave.
But it is too late.
EEEEEEEEEEEEEEEEK!

"Yikes! What a ride!" says Dad.
"It is time to get a nice bite."
Rose, Tate, and Duke eat cake.
Eat, eat, eat!

Then Mom says, "The sun has set.
It is time to get home."
The five beans leap in a big jeep.
BEEP, BEEP!

On the road,
they see five nice people
in a big jeep.
Wave, wave!

The five nice people
see five nice beans.
Wave, wave.
"I like people!" says Duke.
"People are a lot like beans."

Read & Review

Invite your learner to point to each long-vowel word and read it aloud.

a_e

Tate
wake
tale
take
lake
cake
wave
late
brave

ea

beans
leap
eat
seat
meal
read
neat

o_e

Rose
hole
home

i_e

five
like
ride
time
bike
bite
fine
nice
yikes

oa

road
boat

ee

meet
jeep
see
feel
beep
deep
eek

ai

tail

u_e

cute
Duke
huge

Fun Fill-Ins

Read the sentences aloud, inviting your learner to complete them using the long-vowel words in the box.

jeep hole huge five boat

1. The number of beans is ______.
2. At the lake, Tate sees a ______.
3. Duke digs a deep ______.
4. The beans go on a ride that is ______!
5. At the end, the beans wave at five nice people in a ______.